PATTERNS

Ivan Bulloch

Consultants
Wendy and David Clemson

KV-052-234

D1620903

TWO-CAN
in association with
WATTS BOOKS

2 Looking at Patterns

There are patterns all around us.
You can find them in paving stones,
in the stitches of your jumper and on
a butterfly's wings. A pattern is made
when shapes or numbers are put in
a sequence and repeated.

Look around you. How many different patterns can you spot?

Here's what you will learn
We use patterns to help us make sense of the world. Maths is all about patterns. The activities in this book will help you
● sort things into groups
● match similar things
● find out how things fit together.

4 Spiral Snake

Make a patterned snake to hang from your ceiling.

Painting a Spiral

● Draw a spiral on a piece of card. Start from the edge of the card and gradually spiral in towards the centre. You may need to draw a few spirals for practice first.

● Cut the snake out starting from the end of the spiral on the edge of the card.

● Paint a snake pattern on your spiral, or decorate it with coloured paper.
● Ask a grown-up to thread a piece of cotton through the middle of the spiral. Now hang your snake up.

Here's what you learn
Making and decorating spirals helps you
● create repeating patterns
● change a flat shape into a three dimensional one.

6 Beads

Threading beads is a good way to make a pattern. Look around your home or school for things to use as beads. Here are some ideas for making your own beads.

Paper Beads
● Glue together two pieces of coloured paper. Tear out a triangle shape. Roll the shape around a pencil and stick down the narrow end.

● Make a simple paper bead with a long strip of coloured paper. Roll it around a pencil, then stick down the end. You could decorate the paper before making your beads.

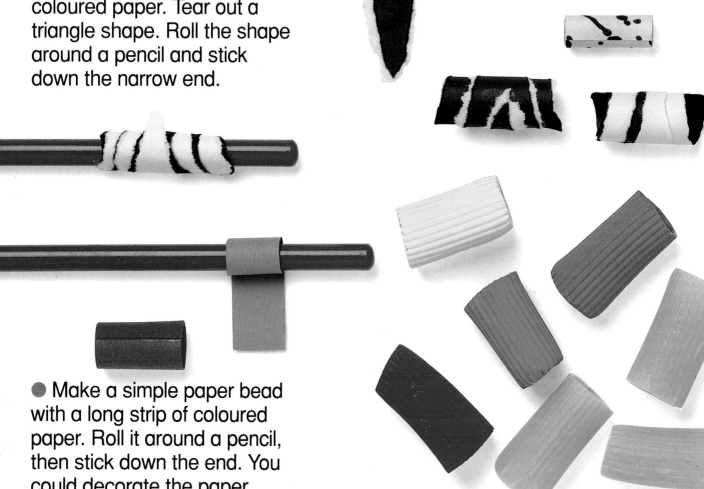

Pasta Beads
● Pick pasta shapes with holes in the middle.
● Paint the shapes with poster paints and leave to dry.

y Beads

Jse the type of clay which dries by
elf to make these beads.

Make a small ball of clay and ask a
wn-up to make a hole in it with a
tting needle or cocktail stick.

Sort Them Out

How many different types of beads
have you collected?

● Sort the beads into different colours
and shapes.

> **Here's what you learn**
> Making and sorting beads helps you
> ● sort things into different groups or
> categories
> ● match similar things.

ads to Find!

ou look, you should be able to find
s of things to use as beads. We
d straws, plastic beads and even
anuts. Can you think of anything
e you could use?

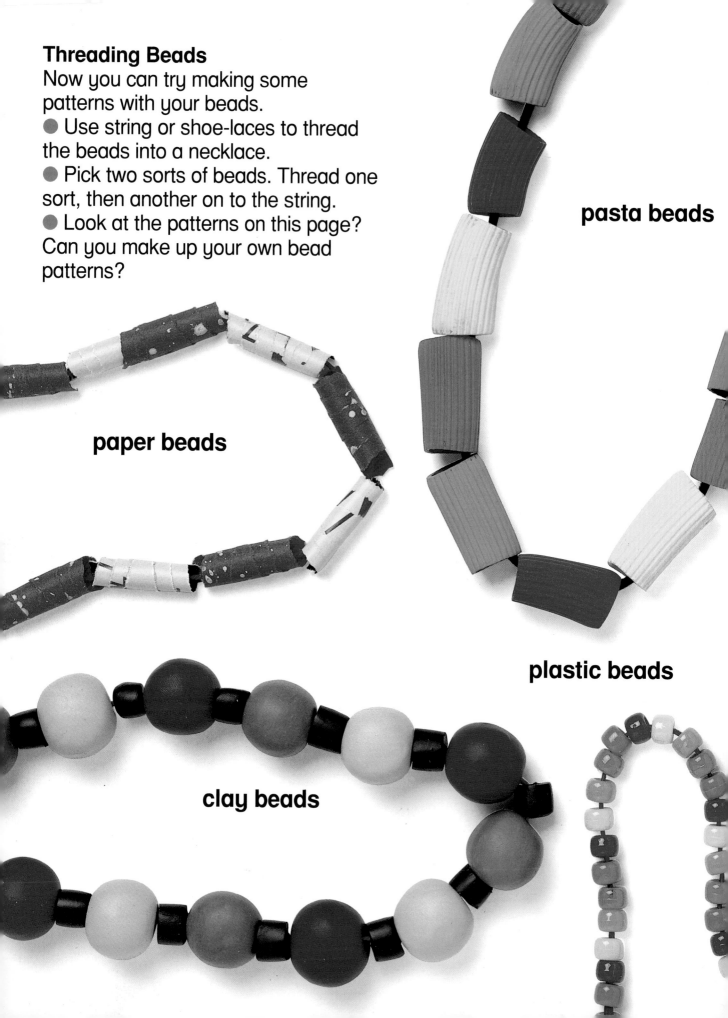

Threading Beads

Now you can try making some patterns with your beads.

● Use string or shoe-laces to thread the beads into a necklace.

● Pick two sorts of beads. Thread one sort, then another on to the string.

● Look at the patterns on this page? Can you make up your own bead patterns?

pasta beads

paper beads

plastic beads

clay beads

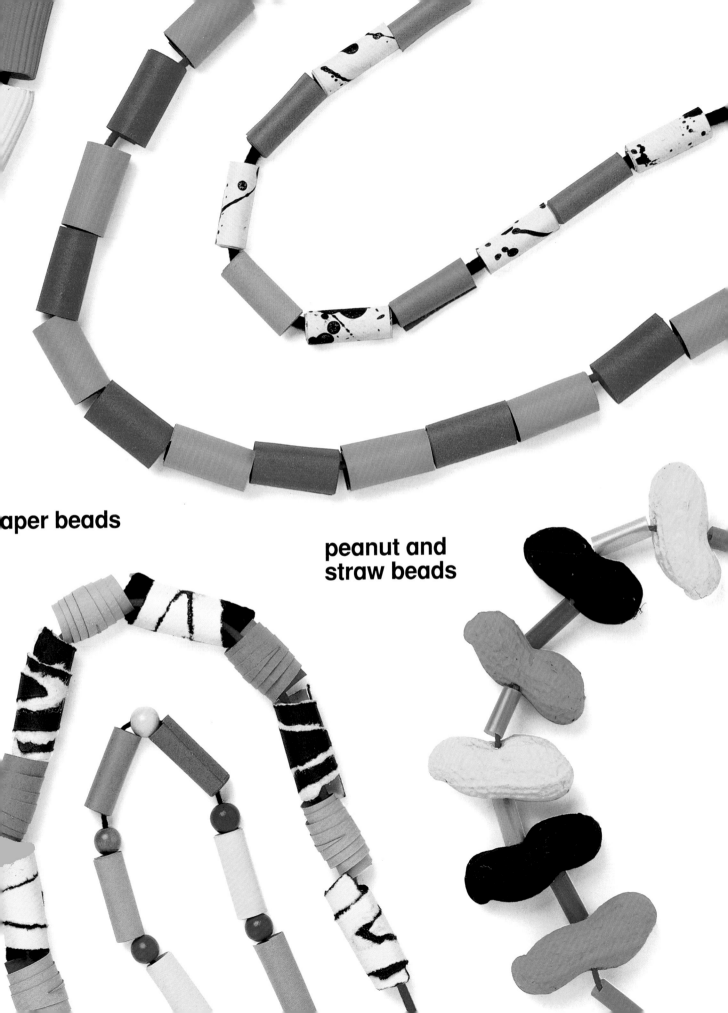

aper beads

**peanut and
straw beads**

10 Cake

Here's a delicious way to play with patterns! Ask a grown-up to help you cover the top of a cake with soft icing. Use a collection of sweets to decorate the top.

Shapes and Colours

First decide which sweets you are going to use. Which ones look good together? Which are your favourites?

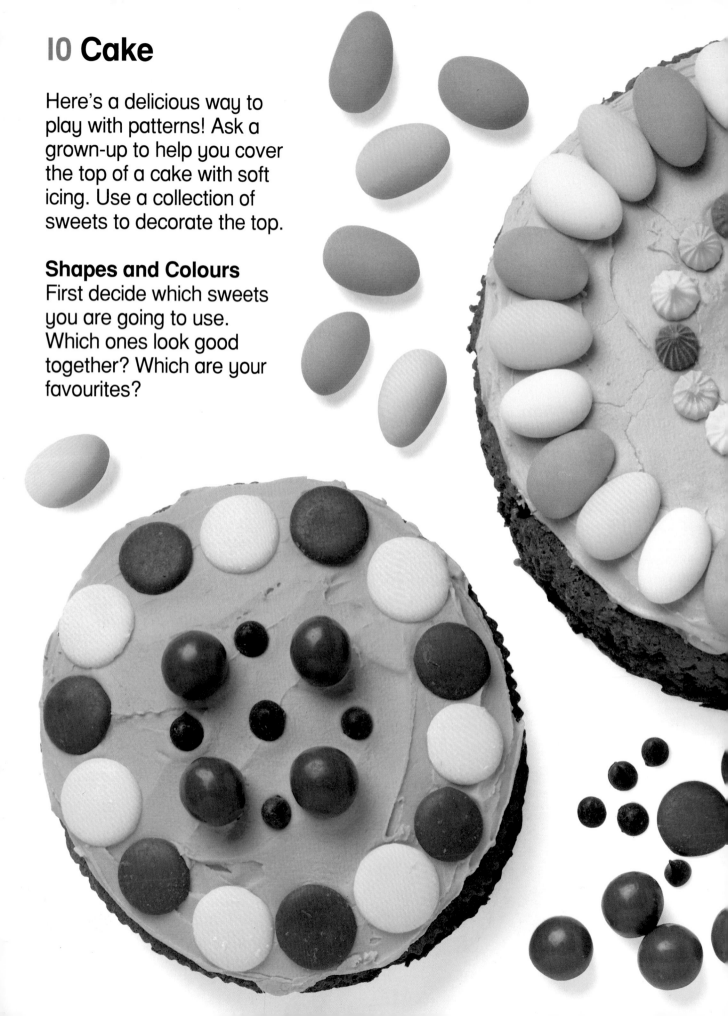

Planning your Pattern

● Start by making a circle of different sweets around the edge of the cake.

● Choose another pattern for the centre of the cake. You could make more circles or use different sweets to make a cross.

Here's what you learn
Decorating cakes helps you
● sort things into groups
● match similar things
● create simple patterns.

12 Weaving

Some of the clothes you wear are made from woven fabrics. These fabrics are made on large machines called looms. You can do your own weaving at home using a cardboard loom. Use brightly coloured wool or strips of felt. Can you see the pattern the threads make?

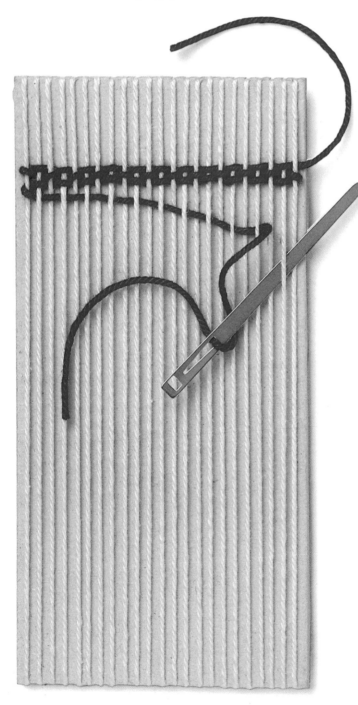

Loom
● Ask a grown-up to cut a small pie of card and make notches in both e
● Wind a length of wool around the card. The notches will keep it in plac Tie the ends of the wool at the back

Over and Under
● Ask a grown-up to thread a large, blunt needle with a length of wool.
● Push the needle under and over t threads until you reach the other sid
● Weave back the other way, under the threads you went over before, a over those you went under.

Here's what you learn
Weaving helps you
● create simple patterns
● use ideas about symmetry.

You can make a pattern with woven paper too! Find some fairly stiff coloured paper to weave with.

Simple Pattern
● Fold a piece of paper in half.
● Make a row of cuts along the folded edge. Unfold the paper.
● Cut some strips of another colour. Weave these strips over and under the slits you have made.

Diagonal Stripes
● Take another piece of paper and make diagonal cuts. Weave strips through the slits. Does the pattern look the same?

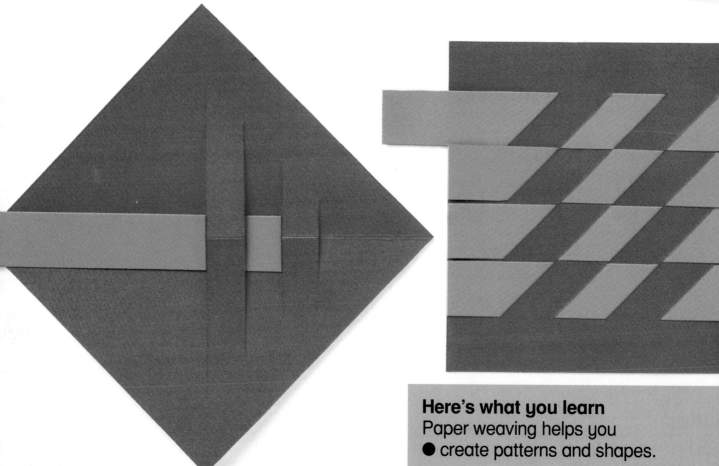

Here's what you learn
Paper weaving helps you
● create patterns and shapes.

avy Stripes

k a grown-up to cut wavy slits in a
ce of paper. You will also need
ne wavy strips of another colour.
eave the strips as before.

rtan Stripes

t two slits close together in a piece
olded paper. Leave a gap, then cut
more slits close together and so
Weave thick and thin strips of
oured paper in and out of the slits.

-zag Stripes

k a grown-up to make zig-zag slits
he paper with a craft knife. Weave
ight strips through the slits.

16 Dot Patterns

Here's another way to make patterns with wool.

Glue Patterns

● Make a pattern with a few dots of glue on a piece of card.
● Take a length of wool. Press one end into the glue.
● Guide the wool around the glue pattern, pressing it down as you go.

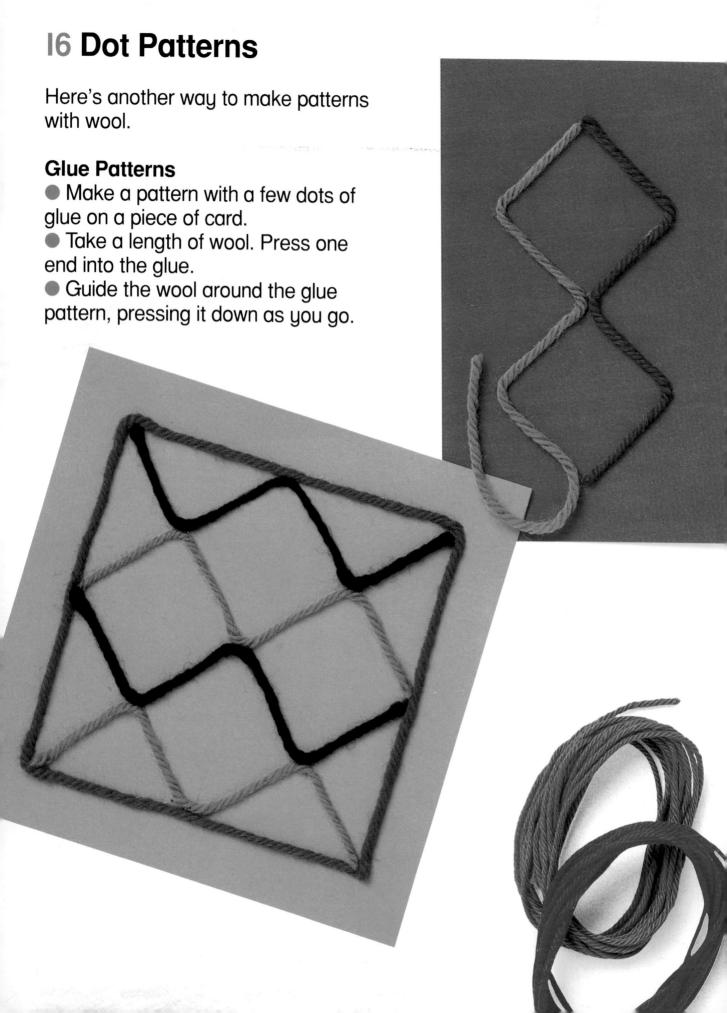

Ask a grown-up to arrange
pattern of pins on a piece
strong card.
Take a length of wool and
it carefully to one of the
tside pins.

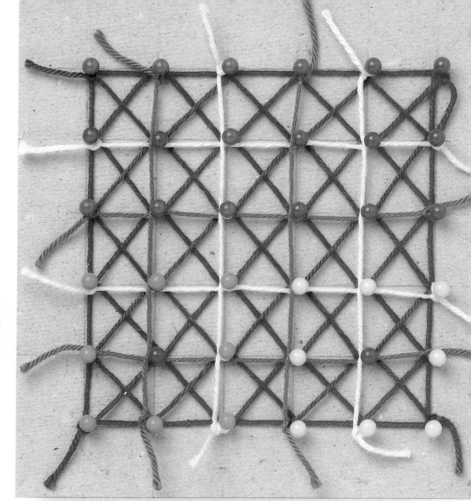

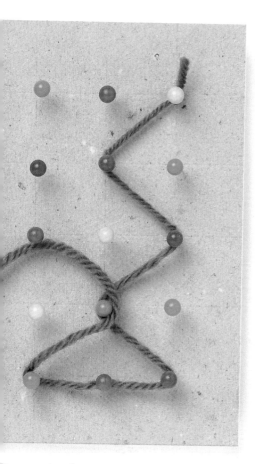

Stretch the wool around
pins, twisting it to keep it
lace. When you reach
edge, tie the end of the
ol, and cut off any extra.

ere's what you learn
aking dot patterns helps
ou
think up patterns
create shapes.

18 Paper Cuts

You can make some amazing patterns by folding and cutting paper.

Fold and Cut
● Fold a piece of paper in half and then in half again. Cut a small piece out of one edge. Unfold the paper.

● To make a more complicated pattern, make several cuts along the edges before unfolding the paper.

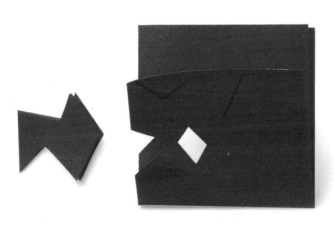

oncertina Folds

Cut a long strip of paper.
ake folds backwards and forwards,
 the strip opens out like a concertina.
Make cuts in the folded paper.
Open the paper out.

Here's what you learn
Making paper cuts helps you
  create patterns
  discover symmetrical patterns.

20 Tiles

Each of these tiles has a very simple design, but you can arrange them to make all sorts of patterns.

Designing the Tiles
● Ask a grown-up to cut out some squares of card, all the same size.
● Choose a simple design and paint each square exactly the same.

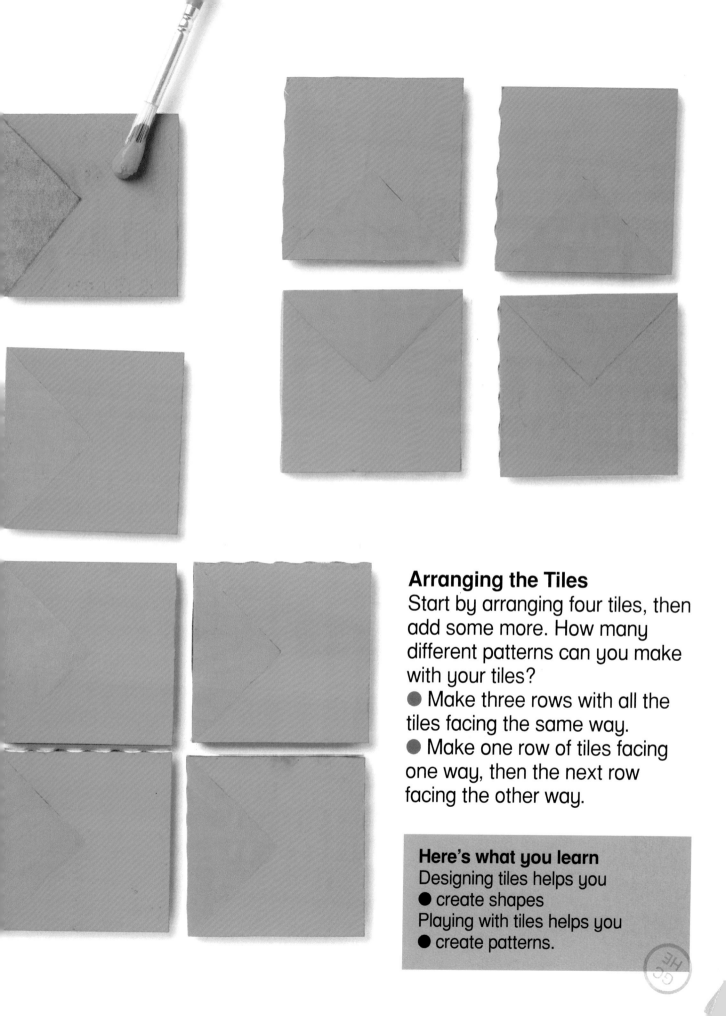

Arranging the Tiles

Start by arranging four tiles, then add some more. How many different patterns can you make with your tiles?

● Make three rows with all the tiles facing the same way.

● Make one row of tiles facing one way, then the next row facing the other way.

Here's what you learn

Designing tiles helps you
● create shapes
Playing with tiles helps you
● create patterns.

22 Mosaics

These coloured shapes fit together to make patterns.

Making the Shapes
Ask a grown-up to cut some shapes from coloured paper or thin card. They could draw around the shapes shown on this page.

Fitting Together
● Sort the shapes out. Put all the triangles together, all the diamonds, and so on.
● See how the shapes that are the same fit together. Use different colou to make a pattern.
● Now try fitting two different shape together. Which shapes fit well?

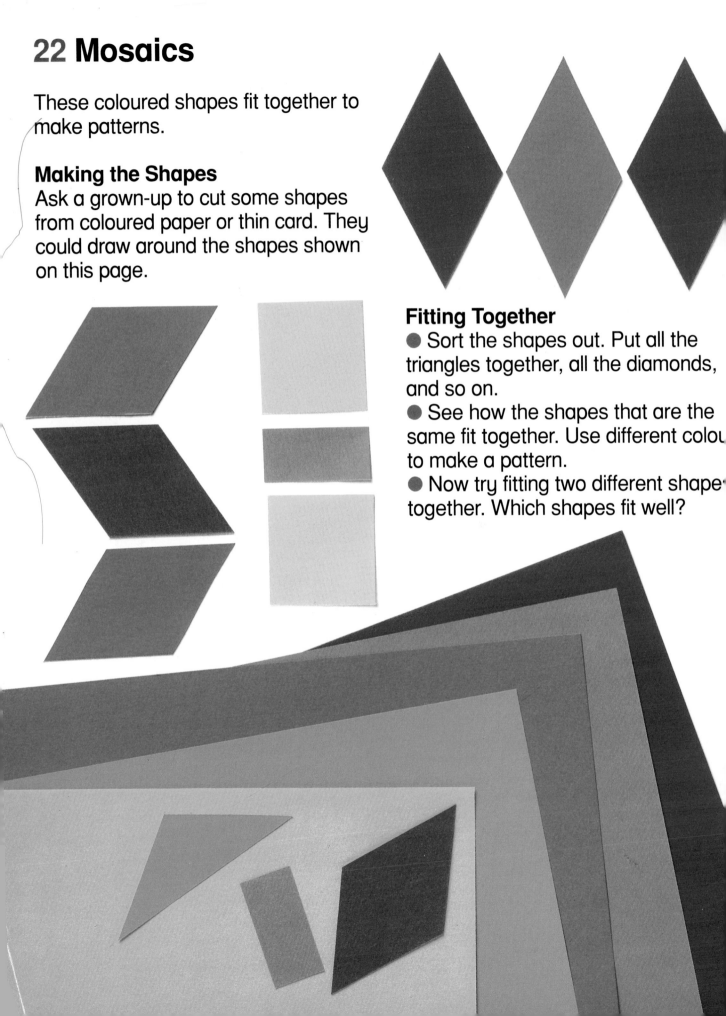

Here's what you learn
Making mosaics helps you
● create patterns
● discover how some shapes fit together,
or tessellate.

24 Wrapping Paper

Make a sheet of wrapping paper by decorating it with a pattern. Pick a shape and repeat it lots of times.

String Blocks
● Glue a long length of string on to a piece of card and let it dry.
● Dip the string into thick paint and press on to a sheet of paper.

Potato Prints
● Think of a simple shape and draw on a piece of paper. Ask a grown-up cut your shape from half of a potato that the shape sticks up.
● Use a paintbrush to cover the sho with thick paint. Press the potato on a sheet of paper.
● Lift the potato off and put some m paint on. Print the shape lots of time

Stencils
● Cut a stencil out of strong card.
● Place the stencil on a sheet of paper. Dab paint over the stencil. Remove it carefully and repeat.

Here's what you learn
Making wrapping paper helps you
● create repeating patterns
● create shapes
● invent new designs.

26 Mirror Prints

These amazing prints are reflections.

Fold and Paint
● Fold a piece of paper in half. Open it out and put a blob of paint on it.
● Fold the paper in half again and press down firmly. Then open it out.

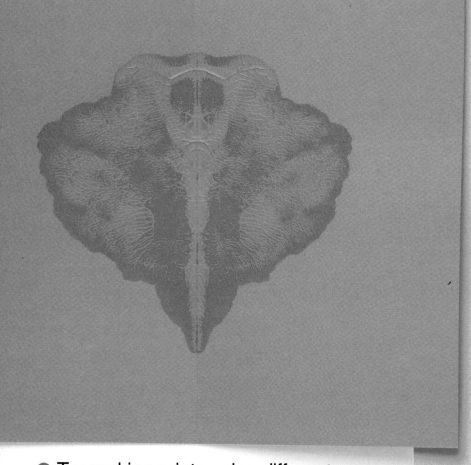

● Try making prints using different colours. Allow one colour to dry before adding the next.

Here's what you learn
Making mirror prints helps you
● discover reflective symmetry
● learn about left and right.

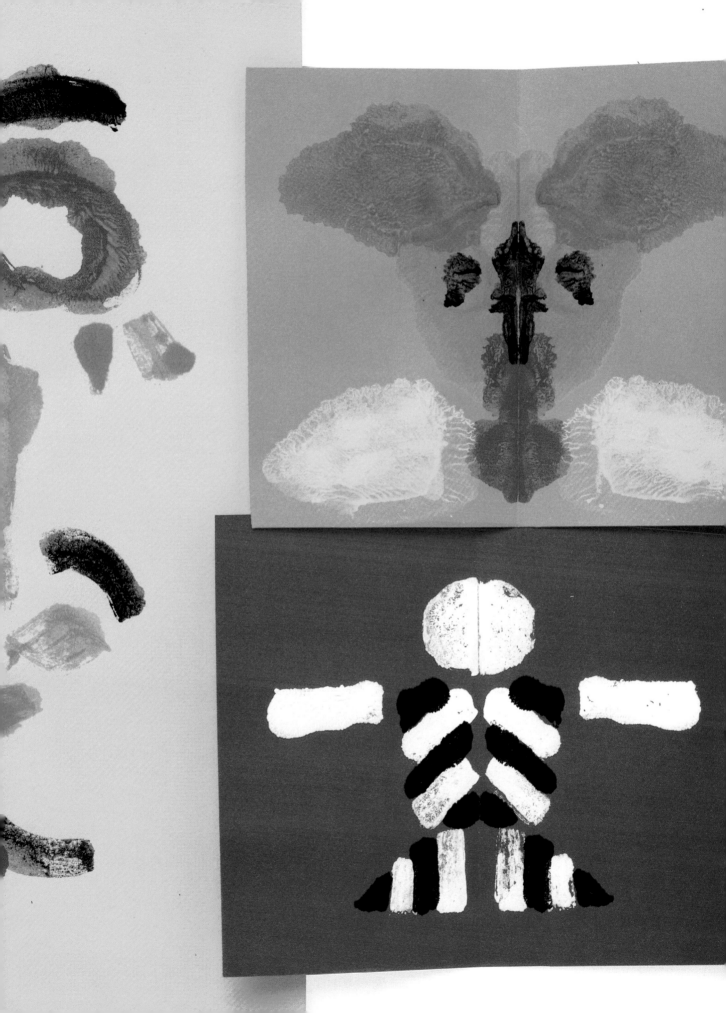

hink up some fabulous patterns to
decorate your T-shirts or socks. Use
fabric paints, and make sure you read
the instructions before you start.

Potato Patterns

● Ask a grown-up to cut a simple
shape from half a potato.
● Cover the shape with paint, then
press it on to your sock or T-shirt.
Repeat to make a pattern.

Here's what you learn
These potato patterns help you
● create repeating patterns
● use familiar shapes
● invent new designs.

Try using different types of patterns to decorate cards, writing paper and envelopes. Use brightly coloured paper and make sure you leave enough room to write on! You could use some of the patterns you have found in this book, or make up some new ones.

● Cut or tear coloured paper shapes. Glue them down in a pattern.
● Use plastic shapes to print.
● Cut out a card stencil. Hold it down firmly and dab on thin paint with a sponge.

Here's what you learn
Decorating stationery helps you
● create patterns
● create shapes
● invent new designs.

Index

Editor: Diane James
Photography: Toby
Text: Claire Watts

First published in Great Britain in 1992 by
Two-Can Publishing Ltd
346 Old Street
London EC1V 9NQ

Copyright © Two-Can Publishing Ltd, 1992

This edition published in 1995 by
Two-Can Publishing Ltd
in association with **Watts Books**

Printed and bound in Hong Kong

2 4 6 8 10 9 7 5 3

All rights reserved. No part of this publication may be reproduced, stored
in a retrieval system or transmitted in any form or by any means electronic,
mechanical, photocopying, recording or otherwise, without prior written
permission of the copyright owner.

A catalogue record for this book is available from the British Library.

ISBN 1-85434-334-3

Measures and the National Curriculum

Creating the patterns shown in this book
directly helpful to National Curriculum
mathematics. Doing these activities
involves interpreting and carrying out
instructions, appraising work, and
developing confidence in craft skills. Thus
children's involvement in other National
Curriculum subjects, such as science,
technology and art can be supported by
having fun with this book.

Contents

Looking at Patterns AT3 level 1; AT4 level 1
Spiral Snake AT4 level 1
Beads AT5 level 1
Threading Beads AT3 level 1; AT5 level 1
Cake AT3 level 1; AT5 level 1
Weaving AT3 level 1
Paper Patterns AT3 level 1
Dot Patterns AT3 level 1; AT4 level 2
Paper Cuts AT3 level 1; AT4 level 3
Tiles AT3 level 1; AT4 level 3
Mosaics AT3 level 1; AT4 level 3
Wrapping Paper AT3 level 1; AT4 level 3
Mirror Prints AT4 level 3
Crazy Clothing AT3 level 1
Stationery AT3 level 1

Consultants

Wendy and David Clemson are
experienced teachers and researchers.
They have written many successful books
on mathematics and are regular
contributors to "eG", the educational
supplement of "The Guardian" newspaper
Wendy is currently pursuing her interests
the primary curriculum and is working on a
variety of writing projects for children,
parents and teachers, with a particular
emphasis on the early years. David is
Reader in Primary Education at Liverpool
John Moores University.